Hazel Townson

DISASTER BAG

Illustrated by David McKee

Andersen Press · London

First published in 1994 by
Andersen Press Limited,
20 Vauxhall Bridge Road, London SW1

British Library Cataloguing in Publication Data is available
ISBN 0–86264–524–7

Phototypeset by Intype, London
Printed and bound in Great Britain by Cox & Wyman Limited,
Reading, Berkshire

Contents

*For Anne Williams and Pam Pollitt
of Shropshire Library Service*

Your library is precious – Use it or lose it!

1

Scared into Action

In the middle of the maths lesson there began a prolonged and deafening clang. Heads jerked up in alarm. There was a second's pause while the message sank in, then people started scrambling to their feet. Somebody's chair fell over and a couple of desk lids banged.

'No need to panic!' said the teacher. 'It'll just be another false alarm.'

On that reassuring note the Bomb Scare drill went smoothly into action and in less than two minutes the whole school was assembled on the playing-field in a biting wind.

Colin Laird shivered, ignoring the excited chatter all around him. Others might think this a lucky escape from a dreary lesson, but he knew better. It was just another step on the road to Disaster. One day there really *would* be a bomb in the school and they'd all be blown to bits.

Colin had come to the frightening conclusion that the whole world was in a mess. These regular bomb scares were just one example of the terrible things which were happening everywhere, from Chernobyl to the Brazilian jungle, not forgetting the hole in the ozone layer. Nations starved, pollution oozed, disasters abounded (only last week there were two earthquakes, three major floods and a whirlwind) and terrorists struck. Every teatime, when the news came on after the children's programmes, weary families trailed across the television screen fleeing from umpteen ghastly happenings.

It was obviously only a matter of time before Colin became some sort of a casualty himself. And here, at last, on this windswept

playing-field, he finally decided that enough was enough. Personal precautions must be taken at once. He had had his fill of walking around defenceless. He would spend all his birthday money on a Disaster Bag.

Of course, it was obvious that he couldn't just walk into British Home Stores or Marks and Spencer's and ask for a Disaster Bag. He would have to use his own ingenuity and put one together himself.

For a recent school trip his mother had bought him a canvas haversack, like the one in which his dad took sandwiches to work, so he decided to fill that with a careful assortment of life-saving items. These included First Aid kit; torch and spare batteries; plastic bottle of filtered water; Swiss Army knife; emergency sustenance (chocolate, nuts, raisins, biscuits and a carton of long-life milk); air-filter mask; whistle, string, matches . . . and so on.

That Disaster Bag, Colin vowed, was to be his constant companion. Indoors or outdoors, it would stay right by his side, even in school and especially in bed, for he had noticed that most disasters seemed to happen during the night.

One particular concern of Colin's involved his dad's job. Mr Laird worked at Moorscale, the Atomic Energy Establishment whose perimeter wall was only a worrying two and a quarter miles from their house. Not that Mr Laird seemed worried; in fact, it was his constant, excessive cheerfulness which bothered Colin. Dad was obviously trying to wring every last drop of fun out of life before it was too late.

As for Colin's mum, she was a nurse at the local hospital and judging from some of the horrifying tales she related nightly over supper (anything from a mass outbreak of salmonella to motorway pile-up victims or radiation sickness), she would no doubt have approved of the notion of Disaster Bags in general. But as she was under the impression that Colin had opened a school savings account with his birthday money, the project had to remain a secret.

When the Disaster Bag was finally put together Colin felt a great sense of relief. Now, at last, he had something to cling to in a frighteningly precarious world. It was the nearest thing he had to a talisman, ensuring his safe passage into manhood . . . or at least into next year.

Yet on the first morning that Colin took the bag to school, he discovered certain snags.

For a start, the bag was heavy. Added to the weight of his books, lunch, football-strip, woodwork overall and half-finished spice-rack, violin, music-case and history project (including a cardboard Roman helmet, inexpertly glued), it made quite a burden. This slowed him down so much that by the time he reached school he was soaked in acid rain. (Ought he, perhaps, to add an umbrella to his life-saving collection?)

Another problem was that the bag attracted unwelcome attention.

'What you got there, Col? Your Batman outfit?'

'He's joined the Ramblers' Union.'

'Nah, he's on his way to drown the cat!'

'Maybe it's dead already. Let's have a dekko, Col?'

He was lucky to reach the classroom with his secret still intact. He tucked the bag neatly under the desk beside his left foot, where he could give it a reassuring tap every time a low-flying plane zoomed overhead or police-car sirens shrieked down the road outside. In spite of everything, it really was a wonderful comfort.

First lesson was history with Mr Stibson who turned out to be in a sarcastic mood. As he toured the classroom examining various projects, the teacher laced his comments with caustic wit.

'We're supposed to be studying Romans, not Morons, Smith!'

'Julius Scissor, Venables? You can cut that out for a start!'

Long before he reached Colin's desk, Mr Stibson's eye fell upon the battered Roman helmet.

'Well, Laird, what's that supposed to be? A Roman nose? Take it out to the front of the class, boy, and let's have a blow-by-blow account!'

'Old Stibbers is on form this morning!' somebody whispered as giggles and titters erupted from all sides.

Poor Colin struggled from his seat clutching the cardboard monstrosity and was so embarrassed that he forgot to mind where he put his feet. One foot caught in the strap of the Disaster Bag, and he finished up sprawling face-down on the floor with the Roman helmet flattened out of all recognition beneath him.

Wild waves of mirth washed over him

where he lay, and Stibbers' voice boomed like a fog-horn over this sea of trouble:

'I wonder if you've noticed, Laird, that wherever you go and whatever you do, disaster awaits?'

'Oh, yessir, I have, sir!' Colin answered in glum agreement.

Maybe the Disaster Bag was going to be more of a hindrance than a help. Yet the bagless alternative was too dreadful to contemplate. How could he – how could anybody – face the future totally unprepared?

That evening there were pictures on the television news of a devastated Mexican town in which the sewers had blown up, hurling cars, buses, buildings and people high into the air. Massive chasms yawned, ruins tottered and rescuers scrabbled through the rubble with bare hands trying to find those buried underneath. It was worse than an earthquake, a typhoon, a couple of battles and a volcanic eruption all rolled into one.

This news item proved a timely reminder

to Colin to ignore all the jeers and jibes of his cronies. Maybe they'd guessed what was in his bag, and were jealous. For – let's face it – if *they* had been buried under that Mexican rubble, they'd have been jolly grateful for a Disaster Bag of their own.

Why, at that very moment there were workmen digging up the road outside school ready to repair the collapsing sewers. Suppose they had left it too late? Suppose the school caved in, with the whole town on top of it? Colin pictured himself trapped under some crumpled skyscraper, yet thankfully still breathing through his dust-free filter-mask. There he lay, locating by torch in his Disaster Bag the vital food and water which would give him the strength to blow his whistle to guide his rescuers, while he patched up his wounds with his First Aid kit and gouged out airholes with his Swiss Army knife. It was a reassuring vision.

And so, despite a poor start, Colin Laird and his Disaster Bag became inseparable. Throughout a solid week of school, they defied all rules and ridicule. They even went for a relaxing Saturday afternoon mooch round the park together (for you never knew when the ground might open up in front of you or a stray Scud missile catch you between the shoulder-blades).

Yet, as Fate would have it, it was then that Colin encountered Becky Briggs, the girl who was to part him from his bag and so set in motion the biggest disaster Colin Laird had ever known.

2

Fatal Distraction

That Saturday afternoon Becky Briggs, who was in Colin's year at school, was busy being environmentally friendly. Dressed in her oldest clothes and wearing a pair of her mother's gardening gloves, she was flanked by two large plastic sacks. Into one she was stuffing all the re-cyclable paper she could find, and into the other all the empty aluminium cans thrown down by ignorant picnickers.

Colin and Becky came face to face on a pathway near the boating lake.

Becky stared at the Disaster Bag.

'Is that for litter, or are you going on your

holidays?' she asked cheekily.

Colin, who could never think up witty retorts until half an hour too late, decided to ignore her. He simply ambled on, but Becky turned and followed him.

'You know what I'm doing? I'm cleaning up the world. Just look at this park! Litter and pollution's everywhere and some of it's your fault. If it wasn't for people like me, we'd have no raw materials left worth using, and we'd all be gasping and smothering and fighting for our lives under tons of stinky garbage.'

Colin stopped and turned pale with dread at this new nightmare which instantly un-reeled across his mind's eye like a cartoon horror-film. It had never occurred to him that you could actually be *completely buried* under ordinary rubbish. Why, you could catch the Plague while you were covered in stuff like that! It must be a thousand times worse than lying trapped under good, clean, wholesome rubble where people had been known to survive for three or four days with

no more than a few cuts and bruises.

'Well, why don't you do something about it instead of standing there with your mouth open?' Becky went on. 'Here, take one of these sacks and start helping me.'

Before he knew what was happening, Becky had thrust the plastic sack of paper into his hand. She even peeled off her left glove and generously offered it to Colin.

'I'm not dressed for it, am I?' protested Colin half-heartedly as he cast an anxious glance over his new jeans and white trainers.

But Becky made short work of that excuse.

'If everybody said that, where do you think we'd all finish up? This world would be one big disaster area.'

Now Colin shuddered. If anybody knew about disaster it was him; he had made an in-depth study of it. For instance, he'd just thought of a new scenario! Suppose nobody picked up all the cans, so they turned rusty in the rain and he went and fell over one, cut his knee and got blood poisoning? And then suppose there was no paper left in the world, so the doctor couldn't write him the vital, life-saving prescription?

'All right,' he sighed, 'I can manage half an hour.'

He turned Becky's mum's left glove round and fitted it awkwardly onto his right hand so that suddenly his thumb seemed to be pointing in the wrong direction. He wiggled his hand into a more comfortable position, then looked about him for somewhere to start collecting.

Scattered on the grass not far away were half a dozen scrunched-up political pamphlets so he began with those. But each time he bent over to pick one up, the Disaster Bag, which he wore strapped diagonally across his back, kept thumping him in the kidneys.

'Why don't you put that thing down?' asked Becky at last. 'You'd get on a lot faster.'

'Not likely! Somebody might pinch it.'

'So what's in it, then? The Crown Jewels?

Or have you been shoplifting down Wool-worth's?'

Colin straightened up.

'This bag,' he said importantly, 'never leaves my side. It could make all the difference between life and death.'

Becky pulled a mocking face.

'Oooh, very impressed, I'm sure! Anyway, even if it's a bullet-proof gas-mask, it wouldn't hurt to take it off your back and put it down in the grass for a few minutes. Besides, it might get damaged, bumping about like that. If you keep it within grabbing distance and move it along with you I don't see what your problem is.'

To be honest, when she put it like that, neither did Colin.

So, as his back was beginning to feel pretty bruised, he did as Becky suggested. He set the bag down at his feet, intending to drag it forward every couple of strides.

For a while he kept a very close eye on the bag, turning round every few seconds to make sure it was still there.

But then he began to warm to his task. He spotted a whole newspaper lying on a bench some distance away, and leapt after it. This led him in turn to a dew-sodden magazine which had been thrown down

under a tree, and he had no sooner picked that up than he spied a whole paperback novel abandoned on a wall. Why, there was enough waste paper in this park to save a dozen rain-forests!

By this time Colin was actually enjoying himself, feeling useful and virtuous and important; and the more enthusiastic he became, the less he remembered to keep turning round and dragging the Disaster Bag forward. Soon he had left it several strides behind. And of course, that was tempting disaster to sneak along after all – which it promptly did, in the shape of a terrorist called Ruby Rugg.

3

Terrorist Plot

Ruby Rugg was an out-and-out villain, although she didn't look like one. At first glance you would have classed her as a middle-aged, harassed and somewhat untidy housewife. Yet under that mild and shabby exterior beat the heart of a fanatic, a person determined to strike out for her principles however much harm that caused to other people. She was already a great soap-box orator and an even greater protest-marcher, twice arrested for clunking policemen on the head with her sturdy banner. But now she had moved on to the deadlier realm of home-made bombs. In fact, at that very moment she was carrying such a bomb in the huge, deep pocket of her shapeless overcoat, a bomb destined to blow up the ladies' lavatories in the Town Hall.

The police were not yet aware of Ruby's existence. Yet Police Constable Duckett was even now following her down the High Street, having mistaken her for a notorious shoplifter who had three times given him the slip on this very pavement. He was determined that she wouldn't dodge him this time, though. Whatever there was in those great, greedy pockets of hers would soon be under scrutiny. In fact, P. C. Duckett felt glory and promotion rushing towards him by the minute.

Yet Ruby, too, was on the alert, eyes darting this way and that as she pushed her way along the pavement. It did not take her long to realise that she was being followed, whereupon she immediately changed direction away from the Town Hall, stepped neatly through the park gates and broke into a convincing jog. In her bulky overcoat she

didn't exactly look like a jogger, but after all there was no law that said what joggers ought to wear. Chin up, elbows bent, legs pumping away like pistons, Ruby ran.

So, in hot pursuit, did P. C. Duckett, and although Ruby was in slightly better shape than he was, she realised that she could not keep up this jogging for ever. The bulky overcoat was definitely slowing her down and capture was looming ever closer. So she would have to jettison the bomb for a while. What's more, she would have to do it *now*, while she was far enough ahead for the constable not to notice what she was up to.

A litter bin might have made a good temporary dump, but alas! the local councillors in their wisdom had removed all the litter bins and substituted notices saying PLEASE TAKE YOUR LITTER HOME!

Ruby began to worry. And then she spotted the perfect hiding-place.

There were two children busily picking up litter near the boating lake, and close behind them, abandoned on the grass, lay a haversack which must belong to one of them. The children were so intent on what they were doing that they were obviously going to be there for some time, so borrowing the haversack for a few minutes was worth a risk.

With one quick snatch, Ruby gathered up Colin's Disaster Bag and retreated with it into the bushes. There she examined its contents, gleefully removed from it a carton of long-life milk and substituted her bomb, which was about the same size. Then she stuffed the milk carton into her pocket where the bomb had been, placed the Disaster Bag back where she had found it, jogged a bit further, and sat down on a bench. From there she could just manage to keep an eye on the haversack.

Among her other talents, Ruby was quite an actress. By the time P. C. Duckett caught up with her, she was gazing in wide-eyed helplessness at the baffling OPEN HERE instructions on the milk carton. Just to make sure the constable knew it really *was* milk and not a bomb in disguise, she shyly asked him for his help in opening it.

Meantime Colin, still intent on his anti-litter-drive, had rashly gathered up a comic with a blob of unspeakable mess inside it. Before he realised what he'd done, the mess had squeezed out all over his glove and halfway up his jacket sleeve.

Ugh!

With wild jerks of his arm Colin shook the glove loose and flung it to the ground. Then he grabbed a handful of grass and started scrubbing at his sleeve. Goodness only knew what horrible viruses he'd just picked up.

Suddenly he looked down and saw that a great gobbet of mess had dribbled down his new jeans and onto one of his white trainers. Now he was furious as well as disgusted.

'Right! That's it!' he called grimly to Becky. 'I'm off!'

Becky looked at her watch.

'You've only done a quarter of an hour.'

'Well, it's fifteen minutes too long! Just look at the state of me!'

Thoroughly disgusted with the entire human race, Colin picked up his Disaster Bag and marched briskly off home for tea.

4

A Terrifying Mix-up

Ruby Rugg grinned as the disappointed constable moved away, mopping a spurt of long-life milk from the front of his tunic.

So far, so good!

As soon as he was out of sight, she leapt up from the bench, eager to reclaim her bomb from the haversack. She could hardly believe her eyes when she saw that the haversack was gone. Why, she'd only taken her gaze off it for a couple of seconds!

Still, mustn't panic! All was not yet lost. The haversack must have belonged to the boy, who was now nowhere to be seen. But his girlfriend was still there.

Trying her best to look casually chummy, Ruby strolled over to the girl and turned on a beaming smile.

'My, my! You're working hard! How nice to see somebody picking up the litter instead of throwing it down. You're obviously somebody who really cares about the state of the world! We could do with a lot more like you.'

Becky made no reply and in fact gave no sign of having heard. Perhaps she was deaf?

'I see your friend's left you to it, though,' Ruby went on in a louder voice.

Still no response.

'There *was* a boy working with you, wasn't there?' Ruby asked innocently. 'The one with the haversack. Of course, boys haven't got the same staying power as girls. He's probably gone home for a snack. Still, he might come back again later if he lives near the park.'

Becky straightened up with a battered can in her hand. She gave Ruby a calculating look, as if trying to decide whether to throw the can at the nosy woman's head or stuff it down her throat. Surely by now every grown-up in the country should know that children were not supposed to speak to strangers?

Ruby must have read her thoughts, for she sighed and explained:

'Look, love, I'm not some sinister kidnapper, I'm just a nice, ordinary person who's interested in the environment.' (Well, that last bit was true!) 'In fact, I'm thinking of writing an article on Britain's litter problem, and seeing that you two seemed so concerned about it I thought it would be a good idea to interview you. Perhaps we could even organise a picture.'

Becky deliberately turned her back, scowling fiercely.

Still not getting the message, Ruby went on pestering. She suggested that she could ask Becky a few questions for her article, such as why Becky was so concerned about litter, how much time she was putting in collecting it, and so on.

'Then you could tell me where the boy lives and I'll catch up with him at home.'

'A likely tale!' thought Becky, who had once been interviewed by the local paper after winning the High Jump at the school

Sports Day. On that occasion she had had to talk into a mini-recorder but could see that Ruby carried no such thing. The whole affair seemed mighty suspicious.

Fortunately, one of the uniformed Parkies was just coming out of the rose garden so Becky ran over to him.

'Hey, Mister, there's a woman bothering me.'

The Parkie peered suspiciously at Becky.

'What woman?'

'A stranger. I've never seen her before in my life. She's pretending to be some sort of a journalist, but she isn't, she hasn't got the right stuff, not even a pencil.'

'Where is she, then?'

'Over there!'

But by the time Becky turned round there was no woman to be seen.

Well, at least the woman had gone, which was something to be thankful for. The Parkie wasn't too pleased, though, and accused Becky of mischief-making.

'You shouldn't go around inventing stories

like that. Ever heard of the boy who cried wolf? You might really need help one day, and then I wouldn't be likely to believe you, would I?'

Becky was furious. Fancy talking to her like that, after all the tidying up she'd done in his rotten, mucky old park! She'd a good mind to empty all the litter out of the sacks again – but of course she didn't; the world's litter problem was Becky's special nightmare. Still, what with one thing and another, she decided to pack up and go home.

This was no help at all to Ruby Rugg. For although Ruby followed Becky at a safe distance, Becky lived at the opposite side of town from Colin. What's more, she had no intention of seeing him again until school-time on Monday. Even under torture Becky would have been no help to Ruby, for she didn't even know Colin's address. Ruby Rugg was in for a most anxious and frustrating Saturday, and the nearer Sunday came, the more she began to panic. Her plans had been carefully made, with the idea of killing as few people as possible, which was why she had chosen the Town Hall lavatories on a Sunday when the building was closed. Now, with the bomb at large, anything could happen. She might even end up getting blown to bits by it herself! She *must* get hold of that bomb before it was too late!

On Sunday morning Colin rose early, intending to go and help out on his grandad's allotment. This was something he always enjoyed, especially since his grandad let him taste generous samples of whatever happened to be growing. Peas, strawberries, gooseberries, tomatoes, apples, pears, even celery . . . that allotment was a wonderland of grub.

All the same, when Colin came downstairs he placed his Disaster Bag on the hall table, ready to collect on his way out. Not even Grandad's allotment was safe from calamity. For hadn't one of Colin's comics recently spawned such horrors as radio-active rhubarb, and mutant man-eating greenfly the size of parrots?

Colin shook some rice krispies into a bowl and started his breakfast. But he hadn't eaten more than a spoonful when the telephone began to ring. His mother went to answer it, as his dad was outside washing the car.

Colin could tell from the tone of his mother's voice that something was wrong. It turned out that the caller was Dad's boss, asking if Mr Laird could work today as there was a bit of an emergency on at Moorscale.

'Emergency?' (The very word turned Colin pale.) 'Well then, I suppose he'll have to come,' agreed Mrs Laird grudgingly. Replacing the receiver, she began grumbling to herself that her husband worked long enough hours as it was. Nine hours' overtime he'd put in already this week, and how could you expect people to give of their best if they were tired out all the time? That was how accidents happened, as she knew better than anyone. All her nursing instincts told her how much her husband needed his day

of rest, but of course she had to pass the message on. Then she worked off her resentment by fiercely cutting sandwiches for the lunch her husband would now need to take with him.

She packed the sandwiches into a plastic box, placed the box in Mr Laird's haversack, added an apple and a slice of cherry cake, and put the haversack ready on the table in the hall.

Mr Laird wasn't keen to lose his day off either, but Moorscale workers did not argue. Whistling cheerfully as ever, he briskly made ready to depart.

'Cheerio then, see you when I see you!' he called as he flung lunch-haversack, jacket and newspaper onto the front passenger seat and drove off in his half-washed, still dripping car.

Five minutes later, Colin also set out for his grandad's allotment. But when he picked up what he thought was his Disaster Bag he realised it felt lighter than usual. He looked inside – and discovered his father's lunch.

5

Kidnap!

'Hey, look! That woman's outside again!' Becky Briggs called to her mother.

'What woman?'

'The one I told you about; the one who followed me home from the park yesterday. She was still hanging around at bedtime last night, too. I spotted her when I closed the curtains.'

Mrs Briggs peered through the window but could not see anyone.

'Go on with you! You're imagining things!'

'No, I'm not!' Becky looked out again and realised that the woman had now disap-

peared. 'I bet she's just dodged round the corner because she saw us looking.'

'Don't be silly! Folks don't carry on like that, except in spy stories. You're always making things up. I sometimes wonder what on earth you'll think of next!'

'It's true, Mum! I reckon she's after a boy from our school called Colin Laird. She thinks I'm his friend but I'm not. He was only helping me with the litter in the park.'

Becky's mother decided to put a stop to this romancing nonsense once and for all. Smiling slyly, she announced:

'Well, if you're being followed you'd better stay in today, then, hadn't you? We don't want you being kidnapped and your dad having to find a million pounds ransom, do we?'

'Stay in?' Becky's face fell. 'Oh, Mum! You promised I could go round to Sandra's this morning. She's got a new computer game.'

'Well, stop your silly stories, then. You just like to be the centre of attention, that's your trouble. What about that time you fetched the fire engine out to our garage and it turned out to be next door's garden rubbish burning?'

'Well, you're always telling me it's better to be safe than sorry. I was in on my own that afternoon, and you'd have had something to say if I'd let the house burn down.'

'You'll turn anything into drama, you will, regardless of how many people you upset.'

Becky sighed. 'Oh, all right, so I made a mistake over the fire – *and* the woman. If I admit it and say I'm sorry, can I go to Sandra's?'

Mrs Briggs glanced out of the window once more and saw that the street was empty.

'Oh, go on with you! And be back by twelve o'clock sharp, not a minute later!' She felt she had just won an important victory.

Becky ran down the garden path and into the street. She checked both ways in case the woman was lurking around, but saw no one.

Maybe she *was* just imagining things. What with all her worries about litter, she had to admit that her imagination had been working overtime lately. Why, only last night she had dreamed that she was standing in their kitchen, up to the waist in rotten food scraps, unable to move as a rat the size of a donkey leapt towards her with blood on its teeth.

Ah! but Becky had *not* imagined Ruby Rugg. Desperate by now, the terrorist was there all right, just waiting for Becky to come out.

The minute Becky turned the corner at the end of the street a hand shot out and grabbed her by the shoulder. Before the poor girl knew what was happening she had been pushed into a car which Ruby Rugg had hired less than an hour ago.

'Sorry, love, but this is a matter of life and death!' declared Ruby grimly as she drove away at speed. 'You're going to have to tell me where to find your boyfriend or you and I will have a whopping disaster on our consciences.'

Clutching the haversack with his dad's lunch in it, Colin ran down the street in the direction of Moorscale. He wasn't so much concerned that his dad would starve as that he himself would be caught napping without his Disaster Bag. That bag had become part of him now; almost like another limb. He wasn't going to lose it without a struggle.

Colin had long suspected that he might be psychic, for he often had weird premonitions. Like the time on school Sports Day when he knew perfectly well before he even started his run that the high-jump bar was going to hit him right across the stomach. Then there was the time he woke up in the middle of the night feeling worried, went downstairs, found the kitchen tap running and a sinkful of water just about to overflow onto the floor. He'd saved the whole family from drowning in the nick of time! Well, right now he had a strange feeling that today was the day; something awful was about to happen, and here he was, totally defenceless without his Disaster Bag. He began to run faster.

A pair of huge wrought iron gates guarded the Moorscale perimeter wall, and in a little brick-built office just within the gates sat a uniformed official whom Mr Laird always referred to as Old Tom.

'Nobody gets past Old Tom without a special permit!' Colin's dad was fond of boasting. 'Nobody! Not the Prime Minister; not even royalty.'

Ah! but Colin was a relative of one of the key Moorscale workers. Surely Old Tom would make an exception for him? Besides, this was a genuine emergency.

As soon as Colin came panting up to the gates Old Tom strode out to confront him.

'Now then, laddie, where do you think you're going?'

'I want to see my dad! It's urgent.'

'Who's your dad, then, eh?'

Colin told him, but the name did not seem to impress Old Tom, whose face grew sterner.

'No members of the public allowed past here, except on Open Days! If your dad really does work here, you should know that.'

'Yes, I do, but I've brought his lunch. He forgot it. It's in here, look!'

Colin started unbuckling the haversack.

Old Tom waved it aside.

'Sorry, laddie! Nothing I can do about it. Not allowed to let anything through these gates without a permit. For all I know, there could be a bomb in that haversack, and then where should we all be?'

'It's only cheese and piccalilli sandwiches, and an apple and some cake. You can take

everything out for a proper search if you like.'

'Can't do that, son! Not my job to go searching members of the public. I don't get paid for that sort o' responsibility. But you needn't worry, your dad'll be able to get something in the canteen. He won't starve.'

'But he's got *my* bag by mistake. I wanted to swap. Can't you ask him to come to the gate for a minute, even if you won't let me in?'

By this time Old Tom was losing patience.

'Look, I've told you NO! Your dad's busy. He hasn't got time to go chasing after you. Now hop it, before I get really mad.'

'But –'

'HOP IT!'

Thoroughly defeated, Colin walked miserably away.

6

Is This the End of the World?

By now Colin's sense of foreboding was immense. He felt as if a great black shape was following him. He even kept casting fearful glances over his shoulder to see if he could catch it looming there. Was this creepy feeling just the result of losing the Disaster Bag, or had he really developed some uncanny sixth sense? He must ask his grandad if anybody else in the family was psychic.

Then an amazing thing happened. He was halfway to his grandad's allotment when a car drove past, then suddenly pulled up ahead of him with an ear-splitting screech and began to reverse. What happened then was so swift and sensational that Colin had no chance to react.

A woman leapt out of the car, snatched the haversack from Colin's shoulder, leapt back into the car, pushed a girl out, then drove off with another deafening squeal of brakes.

The girl, who turned out to be Becky Briggs, was in a desperate state of excitement.

'Colin! Colin!' she yelled, running along the road and hurling herself feverishly towards him.

'Hey, what happened?'

Colin grabbed Becky's arm to haul her back onto the pavement, and was surprised when she kept telling him over and over again that he had just had a lucky escape. For it seemed to Colin that Becky was the lucky one. She could have been killed, bursting from a car like that, then prancing around in the road. Suppose there'd been another car coming up fast behind?

'What do you mean, a lucky escape?'

'You know yesterday when you were helping me with the litter? There was this funny woman hanging about and she put a bomb in your bag when you weren't looking. A bomb! A real live bomb! That's why she just snatched your bag back. She's a terrorist and she was going to blow up the Town Hall lavatories. She hid the bomb in your bag because a copper was after her. That bomb was due to go off at noon today, and there were you, walking about with it on your shoulder. You only just got rid of it in time. It makes me go all shivery to think of it!'

Colin turned shivery, too, with a complexion as off-white as semolina pudding.

'She says she'll have to defuse the bomb now, because the Town Hall's all locked up and she doesn't want to do any worse harm than a few broken basins. So she says it's no use us telling on her because we'll have no proof.'

At this point another horrible thought occurred to Becky.

'Hey, but what if she *doesn't* defuse it? She looked like a real nasty villain to me, and anyway I guess a proper terrorist won't want to waste a good bomb after she's gone to all that trouble to make it.'

Colin felt stunned. He could hardly take in properly what Becky was saying. Then, all of a sudden, the truth hit him right in the imagination.

'A real BOMB?' Now he knew for sure why the black shape had been following him.

The black shape was Death! His dad was about to be blown sky-high, and the whole Moorscale Atomic Energy Establishment with him. Even a small explosion would no doubt start a terrible chain-reaction in a place like Moorscale. The result would be worse than Chernobyl; far worse! In fact, today, this morning, this very morning, was probably the end of the world!

7

Will Nobody Believe Us?

Well, this was no time for secrets! In stammering panic, Colin explained about his Disaster Bag and the two look-alike haversacks.

At first Becky didn't believe him.

'You probably just *thought* you'd mixed up the bags. Nobody could make a mistake like that,' she argued. 'If your bag's a lot heavier, then surely your dad would have noticed when he picked it up.'

'He was in too much of a hurry. He's not supposed to be working today; it's an emergency.'

(Well, that was the understatement of the century!)

'I tried to get the bag back but I couldn't.' Colin went on to describe Old Tom and the impossibility of getting past him.

'Didn't Old Tom search your dad's haversack, then, when he first turned up for work?'

'I don't think they bother searching key workers.'

Colin made his dad's job sound important, although to be honest he didn't really know what it was. Mr Laird could have been a cleaner or a clerk or a sorter of nails for anything Colin knew. (Still, they had called him in for an emergency.)

'But what matters is, my dad's right in the middle of Moorscale with my Disaster Bag! So at twelve o'clock the whole place will blow up. It'll be worse than Hiroshima!' the poor boy groaned at last.

The prospect was so terrible that it was beginning to paralyse Colin's brain. He couldn't think what to do and his feet seemed to be stuck to the ground.

Becky also began to feel panicky. Colin

seemed so sure of disaster that she felt she had better give him the benefit of the doubt. And as he also seemed totally unable to act, it seemed she would have to make the decisions herself. Well, first of all they ought to run back to Moorscale and tell somebody.

Becky grabbed Colin's arm.

'Come on! No time to waste!'

Old Tom was just closing the gates after an in-going van. When he saw Colin his brow darkened.

'You here again?' he roared. 'I thought I told you to hop it?'

'There's a bomb in my dad's lunch-bag,' panted Colin. 'It's due to go off at twelve o'clock.'

'Is there, now?' Old Tom sneered sarcastically. 'I thought you said it was cheese and piccalilli sandwiches?'

'Yes, I did and it was. But what's happened is, he picked up the wrong bag and the bomb's in the bag he's got now.'

'You said he had *your* bag.'

'That's right. It's my bag that has the

bomb in it.'

'It's true!' cried Becky loyally. 'I know
because I just got kidnapped by the woman
who put it there.'

Old Tom thought he had never heard such
a load of rubbish in his life. Bombs and
kidnaps, indeed! Whatever would young
kids think of next? Well, nobody was going

to make a fool of *him* and get away with it.

'All right, that's enough! If you two aren't out of my sight in two seconds flat, I'll pick you up one in each hand and bang your heads together. Maybe that'll knock some sense into you.'

'But, Mister . . . !'

'Oh, come on!' sighed Colin. 'He'll never believe us. We can't waste any more time on him. We'll have to tell the police.'

This was easier said than done. They planned to dial 999 but the nearest telephone box had been vandalised; the receiver lay smashed in two pieces on the floor. Luckily, a few minutes later they did happen to run into a police constable, but even as they blurted out their story to him they could see it was no use. He didn't believe them any more than Old Tom had done. In fact, he gave them a stern warning that there were severe penalties for wasting police time and they'd better not do it again.

'He was an even bigger dead loss than your Old Tom!' Becky moaned. 'So what do we do now?'

'We'll have to tell my grandad. He'll believe us. His allotment's not far from here.'

Becky looked doubtful. What use would an old man on an allotment be? Still, she couldn't think of a better solution, so away they ran.

They were almost within sight of the allotment when Becky suddenly stopped. She

had spotted a car parked on some waste ground nearby. It was a car she was never likely to forget – the car in which she had so recently been captured by Ruby Rugg!

8

A Last Resort

'That's her car!' yelled Becky. 'We'll have to tell her what's happened, for how can she defuse the bomb if she doesn't know where it is?'

'Car's empty!' Colin pointed out in further panic, mixed, however, with some relief. In any case, he didn't think a genuine terrorist would be likely to drive up to Moorscale and make a full confession. All he wanted to do was to find his grandad and have the whole responsibility of this nightmare taken off his shoulders.

'Well, she can't be far away,' argued Becky bravely. 'You wait here in case she comes back, and I'll start looking because I know what she looks like.'

'There isn't time for that!' cried Colin. 'We could waste ages. Anyway, even if you find her you're not supposed to speak to strangers of any sort, much less terrorists.'

'It *is* an emergency, in case you hadn't noticed.'

'Emergency's the word all right! She's sure to be really mad at us over the mix-up, and anything could happen. She could even murder you. Murder the pair of us.'

There was an awestruck silence before Becky continued:

'Yeah, she *said* she didn't really want to hurt anyone, but that's a load of rubbish to start with. Even if you put a bomb in an empty building, what about folks walking past when the bomb goes off? There's always flying glass and stuff. People who mess about with bombs are downright wicked and can't be trusted. Still and all, she's the only one who knows how to defuse that bomb.'

'No she isn't; what do you think bomb disposal experts are for?'

Becky sighed. 'I suppose you're right. Where's this famous grandad, then?'

As soon as the bag was safely in the car, Ruby began to worry about how to defuse the bomb. She had an instruction pamphlet somewhere. Let's hope the whole defusing process wouldn't take long, as time was rushing on and getting pretty close to blast-off. She searched her pockets for the pamphlet, without success. Then she wondered if she'd put it in the glove compartment or dropped it on the floor of the car. A frenzied search eventually proved that the pamphlet had completely disappeared. Only then did she remember that she had considered such a publication as incriminating evidence and had destroyed it, just in case she were caught.

Now what? Ruby knew very well that she could not defuse that bomb without some instructions. After all, she lacked experience, never having had to face such a problem before. If she tried and failed, the whole thing might blow up in her face!

What was the alternative, then?

Well, if she couldn't defuse the bomb, she must bury it somewhere where it was least likely to hurt anyone . . . including herself.

She left the main road, sped frantically away from town and out towards open countryside, parked the car, then trudged as far as she could from civilisation, cradling the bag in her arms as carefully as if it were a wounded baby and glancing anxiously at her watch every couple of seconds. Soon she came to a great expanse of rubble, thistles and fireweed, as barren and miserable a place as she had ever seen. This would do nicely!

Hurriedly she unbuckled the haversack – and almost collapsed with shock when she found nothing but a picnic lunch inside it.

What had those kids done with her bomb? She simply *had* to find it!

Starting a frenzied dash back to her car,

she suddenly caught her foot in a hole, fell over and twisted her ankle. There she lay, out of sight in a hollow, moaning with pain and unable to struggle to her feet. Now she couldn't even raise the alarm.

Colin's grandad was spraying his roses to keep the greenfly down. He had a large plastic canister in one hand and a spray nozzle in the other.

'Oh, you've turned up at last, then, have you?' he grinned. 'I thought you were going to do a bit of weeding for me this morning.'

'Something's happened, Grandad!' Colin blurted out, plunging headlong into the horrifying tale.

Colin and his grandad were the best of friends. In fact, each thought of the other as his favourite member of the family. They trusted each other with all sorts of little secrets. Colin knew, for instance, that his grandad hadn't really given up smoking, as his grandma thought he had, but enjoyed a pipe now and again on the allotment. And Grandad knew that Colin had twice been kept in at school for not finishing his homework.

But friends or not, there are limits to what people will believe. The story about the bomb seemed so far-fetched that Grandad did not take it too seriously. The boy had obviously got his facts wrong and jumped to some wild conclusions.

'Here's a couple of trowels for you and

your friend. A bit of weeding will take your mind off your worries.'

Colin grabbed his grandad's arm and shook it desperately.

'But, Grandad, you've *got* to believe us! Nobody else will. You're the only one left, so you *can't* let us down!'

Grandad hesitated. Young Colin and his girlfriend certainly seemed very upset, and it wasn't like Colin to make up a story such as this. Having himself retired only last year from working at Moorscale, Grandad knew what the risks were up there. He also knew that some people were not keen on having Atomic Energy Establishments near their homes. They were likely to protest in all sorts of ways. Maybe this woman was a protester.

'All right then, tell me the whole tale again, slowly.'

Between them, the children filled in all the details. Becky managed a good description of Ruby, and even remembered the number of the car.

Grandad thoughtfully stroked his chin.

'Well, suppose I decided to give my old friend Bob a ring up at Moorscale? And suppose I decided to mention this bomb? And suppose Bob decided to organise a search, evacuating the premises and starting a major alert? What sort of an idiot do you think I'd feel if it was all a hoax?'

'It *isn't* a hoax!' cried both children together.

'You'd be a hero, Grandad! You'd have saved hundreds of lives, including Dad's, because he's had to go in to work this morning.'

Whether that clinched it or not, Grandad suddenly decided to give the children the benefit of the doubt. Abandoning his green-fly spray, he plucked his jacket from the rustic fence and set off briskly for home with the children close at his side.

9

Double-take

Meanwhile, back in Becky's street, there were more dramatic happenings. Becky's mother had chanced to look out of the window again, just as her daughter was being driven away in Ruby's car. Wild with alarm, Mrs Briggs had noted down the number of the car and had telephoned the police at once.

'My daughter's just been kidnapped! Hurry up and *do* something!'

Police officers quickly arrived at the house, though there were lots of what seemed to Mrs Briggs to be time-wasting questions before a police car eventually set out in pursuit.

It took quite a time to track down the abandoned car, for Ruby had driven wildly in all directions. But at last it was spotted, and two officers then set out on foot searching, as they believed, for a kidnapped girl.

Instead, they found Ruby Rugg, clutching her injured ankle and groaning in agony. Despite their uniforms, Ruby seemed quite relieved to see them, which did not surprise the officers in view of her injury. If they hadn't turned up she could have lain in this deserted spot for days. But Ruby's relief sprang from a different source. She had finally decided that as a terrorist she was out of her depth and had better make a clean breast of everything. Accordingly, she began to gabble wild tales of bombs, which left the two constables utterly baffled. They were supposed to be looking for a kidnapped girl; nobody had said anything to them about bombs.

'All right, just calm down! We're going to help you back to our car, then you can make a proper statement later on.'

They decided to take this hysterial woman to the police station right away and let their superior officers sort it out. For one thing, it was ten to twelve and nearly time for their lunch-break.

10

The Dreaded Hour Strikes

Grandad took a long time to track down Moorscale's boss (his old friend Bob) who was already dealing with one small engineering crisis. But the message finally got through and an immediate alert was set in motion.

Up at Moorscale, the warning siren sounded. It was a terrible noise, which halted people in their tracks, then sent them running. Events were moving quickly at last, though by then it was already ten minutes to twelve. Could the bomb be tracked down and defused in only ten minutes?

'We'll give you a ring as soon as there's

any news,' Bob had promised Grandad.

'Well, at least they know where to look,' Grandad tried to comfort the worried children. 'They'll go straight to that lunch-bag, don't you fret!'

After five agonising minutes, Grandad's telephone rang. Becky and Colin froze with anxiety and Colin's heart definitely missed a few beats. Was this the vital call?

But no; it was only Colin's mother, announcing that she had just been asked to report to the hospital at once on standby duty in case any casualties turned up from some mysterious new Moorscale emergency. So could Grandad please give Colin his lunch and keep him there until she collected him later?

Another five minutes ticked leadenly away, and at last the wheezy old clock on Grandad's mantelpiece began to strike twelve.

Becky and Colin dived under the table. Colin dropped his head on his knees, stuck his fingers in his ears and screwed his eyes up tight, tormenting himself with visions of his missing Disaster Bag, needed now as never before. Becky crossed her fingers and said a prayer. Even Grandad moved away from the window in case of flying glass.

Yet no explosion sounded. Surely they would have heard it, from only a few miles away? The suspense was terrible.

By ten past twelve, after what seemed a lifetime of waiting, Colin was a changed boy. In those ten minutes he had had more than enough time to think. For one thing, he had realised that if he hadn't insisted on a Disaster Bag he would never have been mixed up in this horror in the first place. Could it be that the more precautions you took, the worse your prospects became?

At long last the telephone rang again and Grandad's friend Bob told him that the bomb was found.

'Some bomb!' he laughed. 'You should have seen it! It was obviously put together by a bungling amateur who didn't know the first thing about explosives. Pathetic, it was!

Couldn't have blown a butterfly off a blue-bell. Mind you, it's made us realise there's a loophole in our security system. No more lunch-bags will ever be allowed in here. All our workers will have to use the canteen in future, whether they like it or not. So thanks for that – I guess we're really in your debt.'

'Don't mention it!' chuckled Grandad, giddy with relief.

He bent over the table to pass on the

good news that the crisis was over, and the children thankfully crawled out.

'Phew! That was scary!' admitted Becky. 'You know, while I was lying under that table I kept wishing I had a Disaster Bag, just in case. It made me realise what a good idea it is. No sensible person should ever be without one. I'm going to start saving up for one right away.'

'You needn't bother,' grunted Colin. 'You can have mine.'

'But – what will *you* do then?'

'I'll take my chance, like everybody else. You can't go around feeling scared to death all the time; it's a pain in the neck. There's lots more useful ways to channel your energy. Anyway, I could have finished up looking like the Hunchback of Notre Dame. That bloomin' bag weighs a ton.'

'Especially with a bomb in it,' Grandad grinned. 'You did well to call it a Disaster Bag!'